London Sticker Book

Rosie Dickins

Edited by Simon Tudhope

Photography by Stef Lumley
Consultant: Peter Matthews, Musuem of London

About this book

This sticker book tells you about lots of places, people and
things you can see in London. There is also a map of central
London to show you where the main sights are.

On the street

London is an old city. Cobbled alleys run beside tarmac roads, and wherever you look there are reminders that this place is not just thriving now – it has been for centuries.

Flag

Government offices and embassies often have flags outside. Look for the Union Jack, which is the British national flag.

Double-decker bus

The first London bus ran in 1829. It was called an "omnibus" and was pulled by horses. Over five million people use London buses every weekday.

Letter box

The British mail is called the Royal Mail, because it's run with the permission of the king or queen. Letter boxes are marked with the royal crest (sign).

Street theatre

Musicians, acrobats and "living statues" perform in busy areas such as the Covent Garden Piazza.

Plane tree

Plane trees have large, broad leaves and flaking bark. They line many London streets and are home to lots of birds.

Pub sign

There are about 2,000 different pubs in London and most have a painted sign outside. Some gave their name to a district, such as "The Angel" in Angel Islington.

Old sign

In days gone by, many people couldn't read, so buildings had picture signs to help. Some old places still have their signs today.

Metropolitan policeman

Some of the policemen in London wear tall helmets. These helmets are a modern version of the top hats that policemen wore long ago.

Phone box

There are lots of different phone boxes in London. Some old red ones have heavy iron doors and the royal crest.

Cannon bollard

The oldest bollards in London were once ships' cannons. The round part on top is a cannonball.

Virginia Stephen (VIRGINIA WOOLF) 1882 - 1941 Novelist and Critic lived here 1907-1911

Blue plaque

The houses where some famous people lived are marked with a blue plaque.

Taxi cab

Taxi cabs are traditionally black. The sign on top lights up when the driver is looking for a passenger.

Town house

Many town houses were built in the 18th century. You can recognize them from their arched window, called a "fanlight", over the door.

Underground station

This is the sign for an underground railway station. London was the first city to have an underground train service. It opened in 1863, and today there are 270 stations.

Street lamp

Some old street lamps have strange decorations. Iron fish wrap around the lamps along the Embankment.

Along the river

The River Thames flows across London from east to west. Cargo ships and pleasure boats chug side by side between its wide banks.

Cutty Sark

Built in 1869, the Cutty Sark is one of three surviving clippers (a type of fast sailing ship). She used to carry tea from China, but now she's on show at Greenwich.

Sphinx

Two sphinxes guard Cleopatra's Needle (see below). The sphinx was a mythical Egyptian creature with a human head on a lion's body.

London Eye

The largest ferris wheel in Europe. It turns slowly to give passengers time to take in a spectacular view of London spread out below them.

Cleopatra's Needle

This ancient Egyptian monument was brought to London in the 1870s, and stands on the Embankment. The Victorians buried a time capsule underneath it.

Golden Hinde

A replica of a famous Elizabethan galleon that sailed around the world. Sir Francis Drake was her captain.

South Bank Lion

This huge, stone statue used to be on the roof of the Red Lion Brewery. It was originally painted red.

HMS Belfast

A cruiser used in the Second World War. You can explore all nine decks, from the Captain's Bridge at the top to the engine rooms at the bottom, below the waterline.

Tower Bridge

Tower Bridge opens in the middle to let ships through. The road across is often shut several times a day so the bridge can be raised. It took eight years to build and was finished in 1894.

Docklands

This is where the old docks were, but now it's full of modern buildings. The 235m (771ft) tower of Canary Wharf is the tallest building in Britain.

Millennium Bridge

Built to mark the year 2000, the Millennium Bridge spans the river between Saint Paul's Cathedral and the Tate Modern art gallery.

Tate Modern

An art gallery that displays some of the world's best modern art. The building used to be a power station.

Globe Theatre

This is a replica of the building where Shakespeare's plays were first performed. The plays are still put on each summer, and there's a tour of the theatre all year round.

Thames Barrier

Strung across the river near Greenwich, the Thames Barrier has a row of gates that are raised to protect London from floods.

City of London

The City of London is a small district nestling in the middle of London. It's the oldest part of the capital, and is now an important business quarter.

Bank of England

This is where the government keeps its money. It's known as "the old lady of Threadneedle Street", and its vaults are filled with gold.

Monument

Built to mark the Great Fire of London, which destroyed four-fifths of the City in 1666. There's a viewing platform at the top.

Prince Henry's Room

This medieval building was one of the few to survive the Great Fire of London.

City arms

The City's coat-of-arms is on walls all around the district. Statues of dragons (like the ones above) guard the main routes into the City.

Saint Bride's

Designed by Sir Christopher Wren, who also designed Saint Paul's Cathedral. Its steeple inspired one baker to make the first tiered wedding cake.

Roman wall

The Romans built a high stone-and-brick wall around the City. Parts of the wall are still standing.

Swiss Re Building

This is one of the newer buildings in the City. It's nicknamed "the Gherkin" because of its shape.

Saint Paul's Cathedral

Saint Paul's is the cathedral of the City of London. Two million people visit it each year, and its dome has become a national landmark.

Wellington's statue

A statue of the Duke of Wellington stands in the nave (main hall). He's riding on Copenhagen, his horse.

Wren's monument

Christopher Wren designed Saint Paul's to replace the old cathedral destroyed in the Great Fire. His monument reads: "If you seek his monument, look around you."

Mosaics

Parts of the ceilings are decorated with mosaics, which are pictures made from tiny pieces of glass.

Ball and cross

The ball and cross on top of the dome weigh the same as seven cars. A huge brick cone hidden inside the dome stops them plummeting through the hollow roof.

Dome

The dome of Saint Paul's is 111.3m (365ft) high. Inside is a huge gallery where the faintest whisper can be heard all around its curved walls.

Bell towers

Two bell towers stand proud at the front of the cathedral. The right tower houses the biggest bell in England, called Great Paul.

Memorial Chapel

The American Memorial Chapel is dedicated to Americans who died in the Second World War.

Westminster

This is the home of the British government. The Palace of Westminster (the Houses of Parliament) is where laws are made, and kings and queens are crowned in the Abbey.

Coronation chair

Kings and queens sit on this ancient wooden throne to be crowned.

Westminster Abbey

The Abbey has been an important religious building for nearly a thousand years. Kings and queens have been crowned here since 1066.

Edward's tomb

This is the tomb of King Edward the Confessor, the founder of the Abbey.

Palace of Westminster

The Palace of Westminster is covered in intricate stone carvings. Inside there are two chambers, called the Upper House and the Lower House, where Britain's laws are made.

Westminster Bridge

Westminster Bridge crosses the River Thames next to the Palace of Westminster. It was built in the 1800s.

Poets' Corner

Many of Britain's finest writers are remembered in the Abbey, in a place called Poets' Corner.

Big Ben

Big Ben is the huge bell inside the clock tower of the Palace of Westminster.

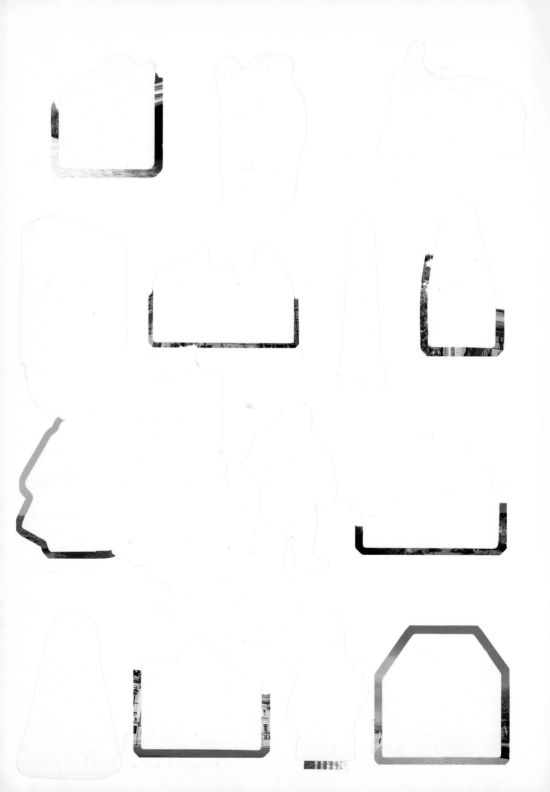

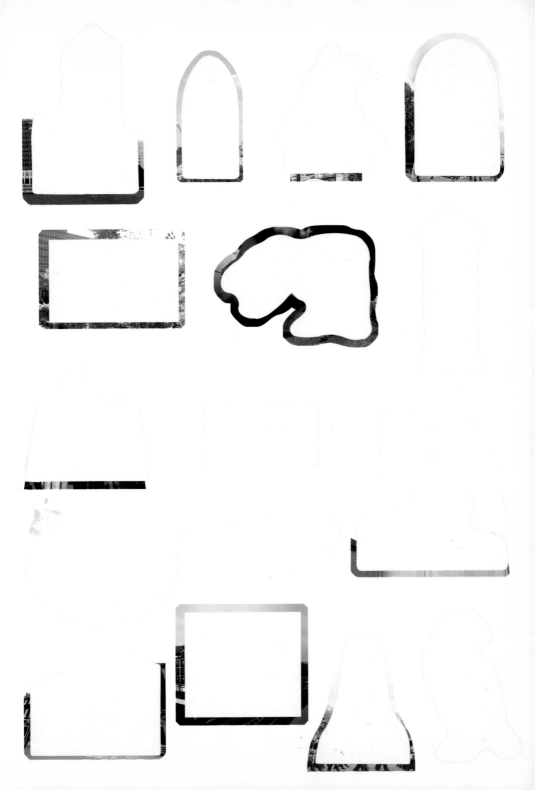

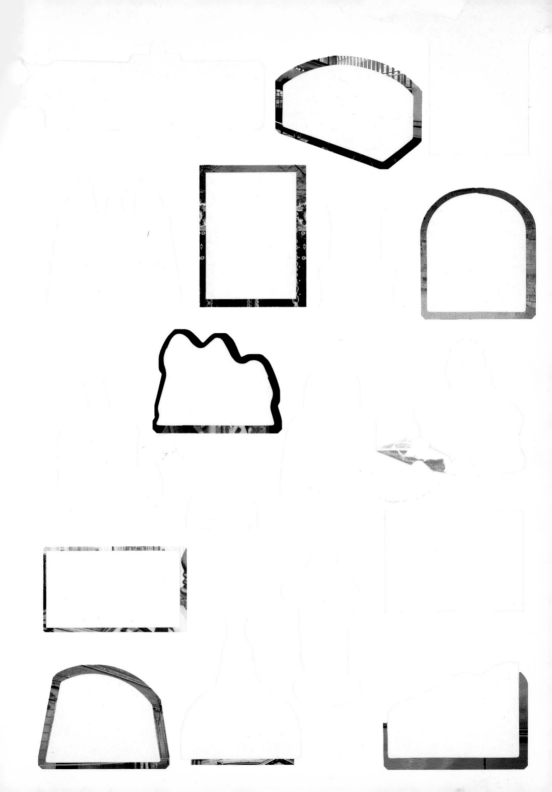

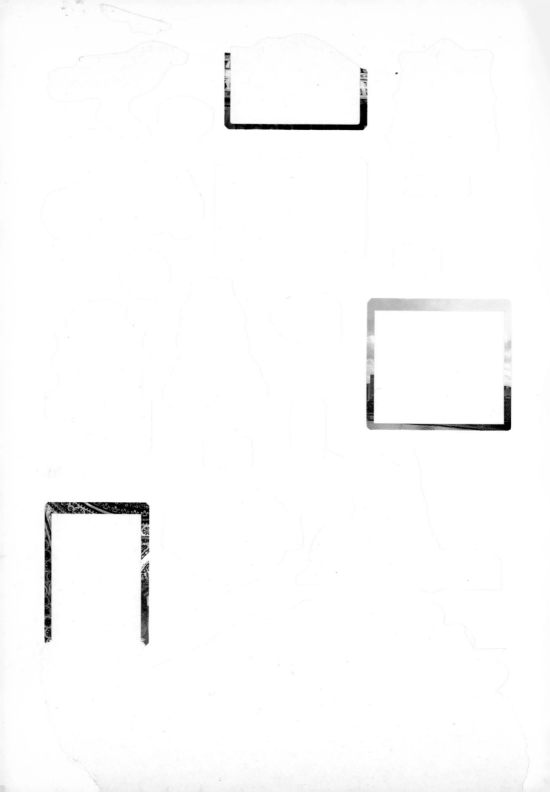

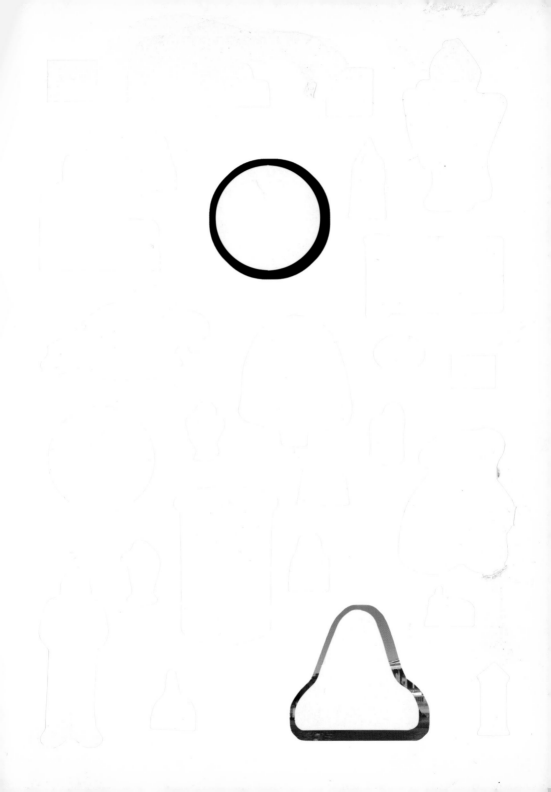

Trafalgar Square

Trafalgar Square was built in the 19th century. It was named after a British victory, led by Admiral Lord Nelson, at the Battle of Trafalgar in 1805.

National Gallery

This gallery on the north side of the square displays some of the most beautiful and valuable paintings in the world.

Nelson's Column

One of the most famous landmarks in London, measuring 52m (170ft) from the base of the column to the tip of Nelson's hat. It shows Nelson with only his right arm, because he lost his left one in battle.

Close-up

The lions

Four lions guard the base of Nelson's Column. They're made from metal taken from the guns of old battleships.

Saint Martin-in-the-Fields

This church, built in 1721, is well-known for its work with the homeless. Its design inspired many similar churches in America.

Fountains

There are two fountains in the square. Both were designed in the 1930s.

Pigeons

Thousands of pigeons live by the square, growing fat on crumbs dropped by sightseers.

Tower of London

The Tower of London dates back to 1078. It's been used as a royal palace, a zoo, a weapons store and a prison.

Block and axe

In the armoury you can see a block and axe that were used to execute prisoners at the Tower.

Crown Jewels

The Crown Jewels are very old and valuable. They include the crown used at the coronation of kings and queens, and the orb and sceptre they hold in the ceremony.

Beefeater

These are the Tower guards. Their official name is the Yeomen Warders, and their uniforms are blue or red.

Armoury

Once used to store suits of armour and weapons. Some are still on display, including a suit made for King Henry VIII.

White Tower

The oldest building on the site, built for William the Conqueror over 900 years ago. Henry III had it painted with whitewash.

Traitors' Gate

Leads from the river into the Tower. Prisoners accused of treason and other crimes were brought through these gates.

Ravens

Six ravens live in the Tower. Legend says that if they leave, the Tower will fall.

Buckingham Palace

Buckingham Palace is where Queen Elizabeth II lives. It's been the official home of British kings and queens since 1837.

The Palace

Once a town house, but rebuilt as a palace in the early 1800s. Most of it is private, but you can visit the Royal Mews (stables) and the Queen's Gallery.

Canada Gate

The Canadian government gave this gate to Queen Victoria in 1897 for her Diamond Jubilee (60th year as Queen). It leads into Green Park.

Foot Guard

These guards wear old-fashioned red jackets and tall, furry hats called "bearskins".

Changing of the Guard

When new guards come on duty there is a ceremony called the Changing of the Guard. You can watch it most mornings.

Victoria Memorial

Queen Victoria was the first queen to live at Buckingham Palace. There's a memorial to her in the Queen's Gardens.

Household Cavalry

The Queen's Household Cavalry are mounted guards. You can see them at the Horse Guards Parade.

Royal Standard

This is the Queen's flag. It flies over the central balcony when the Queen is at home.

More things to see

There are lots of things to see and do in London apart from the famous landmarks. Here are a few of the most popular:

British Museum

The world's oldest public museum displays historical objects from many cultures, including a collection of ancient Egyptian mummies.

London Zoo

Over 650 different types of animal, including blackfooted penguins, live here, in one of the world's oldest zoos.

Science Museum

With exhibits ranging from pocket calculators to real spacecraft, this museum displays a host of scientific marvels.

Peter Pan

In Kensington Gardens stands a statue of Peter Pan, the Boy Who Never Grew Up, from the story by J.M. Barrie.

Pirate Ship

Part of a playground built in memory of Diana, Princess of Wales, the ship is surrounded by a paddling pool.

Harrods

Harrods first opened in 1849. It's one of the grandest department stores in Europe, and claims to sell everything.

Museum of Childhood

This museum in Bethnal Green displays toys from through the ages, from puppets and puzzles to teddy bears, dolls' houses and dolls.

Royal Air Force Museum

The museum at Hendon has over 100 real aircraft, including Spitfire and Hurricane fighter planes, a Vulcan bomber and a Harrier Jump Jet (shown below).

London Dungeon

In the dungeons you can retrace the footsteps of legendary murderers Jack the Ripper and Sweeney Todd, as well as take a boatride through Traitors' Gate (see page 10).

(see page 10).

Natural History Museum

Inside a grand red brick building loom full-size skeletons of some of the biggest dinosaurs that ever walked the Earth. There are also robotic models that show how they moved.

Museum of London

This museum tells the story of London. The Lord Mayor's coach is among the exhibits.

Tate Britain

Tate Britain displays works of art by famous British artists from Tudor times to the present day.

Little Angel Theatre

The theatre at Angel Islington puts on captivating shows using puppets of all kinds.

Madame Tussaud's

Madame Tussaud's is the world's most famous wax museum. It's full of lifelike wax figures of famous people, from actors, models and sports stars to the royal family.

Map of central London

This map shows all the sites described in the book. To find out more about visiting these places, ring the London Tourist Board on 08701 566 366, or look up details on the internet at: www.visitlondon.com

Websites to visit

If you have access to the internet, you can get a preview of many of these sights online. Go to www.usborne-quicklinks.com and enter the keywords "London sticker" for links to some of the best London websites.

Here is the key to the places marked with numbered circles on the map.

1. London Zoo
2. Madame Tussaud's
3. Peter Pan's Statue
4. Pirate Ship
5. Science Museum
6. Natural History Museum
7. Harrods
8. Buckingham Palace
9. Victoria Memorial
10. Horse Guards Parade
11. Westminster Abbey
12. Tate Britain
13. Palace of Westminster
14. Nelson's Column
15. National Gallery
16. Hamleys toy shop
17. Saint Martin-in-the-Fields
18. British Museum
19. Covent Garden Piazza
20. Saint Bride's Church
21. Cleopatra's Needle
22. London Eye
23. South Bank Lion
24. Westminster Bridge
25. Tate Modern
26. Globe Theatre
27. Millennium Bridge
28. Golden Hinde
29. London Dungeon
30. HMS Belfast
31. Tower Bridge
32. Tower of London
33. Monument
34. Bank of England
35. St Paul's Cathedral
36. Museum of London
37. Swiss Re Building

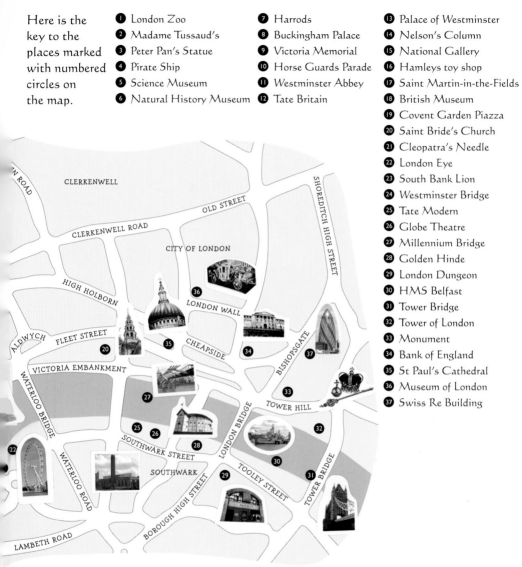

What's on London websites

- Explore the Tower of London's long and bloody history.
- Find out about the National Gallery and see pictures from their collection.
- Take a peek inside Buckingham Palace.
- Meet the animals of London Zoo.

- See 360° bird's-eye views over London, taken from the top of the London Eye.
- Watch videos of old moving toys in the Museum of Childhood.
- Watch flesh-eating beetles and leaf-cutting ants on a live webcam at the Natural History Museum.

Index

Cover design: Joanne Kirkby

Additional photographs copyright © Allan Baxter / Digital Vision / Getty Images (Cover), The Golden Hinde (5),
© www.aviewoncities.com (Swiss Re Building 6), © 2003 Wilfred W. Lam (Saint Paul's bell towers 7, Big Ben 8); Joshua Cardale
(Nelson's Column 9), Photograph by Sgt Ian Liptrot © Crown Copyright/MOD, Reproduced with the permission of the Controller
of Her Majesty's Stationery Office (Horse Guard drummer 11), Harrods (12), The Science Museum (12, 14), The Zoological Society
of London (London Zoo 12, 14), The Trustees of the Victoria and Albert Museum (Museum of Childhood 12), The Museum of
London (13), The Royal Air Force Museum (13), The Natural History Museum (13) and the Little Angel Theatre (13).
Additional illustrations by Linda Penny and Trevor Boyer. Thanks to Brian Voakes, Stuart Spinks and Louie Stowell.